How a Tree Grows

by Yoon Gil
illustrated by Ana Ochoa

It is fall.

"What is this?" said Mack.

"It is an acorn," said Dad.
"We can plant it. Then it
will grow into an oak tree."

"Where can we plant the acorn?" said Mack.

"We need a sunny spot," said Dad.

It is winter.

Mack can see the
red flag in the snow.
The red flag shows the spot
where the acorn was planted.

It is spring.

Mack sees the red flag
in the grass. Mack
can water that spot.
He can give that spot
a little water every day.

It is summer.

"Look," said Mack.
"I see a stem!
I see leaves!"

Dad said, "The plant will get
a little bigger every year."

"So will I," said Mack.

It is fall again.

The little oak tree has
red leaves.

It is winter again.

"Look," said Mack.
"The little tree has no leaves."

Dad said, "The big oak tree has no leaves. Oak trees rest in the winter."

It is spring again.

Mack said, "Look!
The little oak tree
has a lot of leaves."

"The leaves make food for
the tree," said Dad.

It is summer again.

"I am bigger now. The tree is bigger too," said Mack.

It is fall again.

"Look," said Mack. "My tree has red leaves again."

"The big oak tree has red leaves too," said Mom.

"My oak tree will be big one day," said Mack.

"Look at this!" said Kara.

"It is an acorn, Kara. We can plant it," said Mack.

"Where can we plant it?"
said Kara.

"We need a sunny spot,"
said Mack.